USBORNE KEY ...
Practice ...
Spelling

Written by Kirsteen Robson

Illustrated by Maddie Frost

Designed by Karen Tomlins

Series Editor: Felicity Brooks

Once you've completed an activity sheet, you can check your answers at the back of the pad. You'll also find a complete list of all the words in the pad and some useful spelling practice tips.

Here are the animals you'll meet in this pad.

Coco the raccoon

Bun the rabbit

If you want, you can tear off the sheets to take out with you so you can practise wherever you are.

Olly the owl

Foxy the fox

Mo the mouse

Moley the mole

Squilly the squirrel

Hug the bear

Stripe the badger

Spike the hedgehog

Grown-ups – when you practise spelling sounds with your child, say the letter sounds and not the letter names (say 'sss' not 'ess').

Missing beginnings

Help Mo choose the right letter from the boxes to start each word. Then, practise the spellings on the dotted lines.

....e g

....

....i n

....

....o p

....

....u t

....

....e s

....

m

n

y

l

f

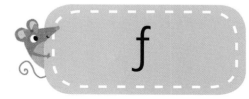

k or c?

Sometimes, the letter **c** makes a sound like a **k**. Can you help Coco choose a **c** or a **k** to start her words? Then, practise spelling the words under their correct starting letter.

...ar

...og   ...ing

...ey

...eep   ...url

c

k

. . . .

. . . .

. . . .

ll and ss words

Say each word out loud and look at it carefully. Then, cover it and try spelling it on the dotted line. Uncover your word to check if your spelling is right. Turn the page over to practise again.

1 ill

2 hill

3 pill

4 mess

5 miss

6 moss

1

....

2

....

3

....

4

....

5

....

6

....

Twit twoo!

After you have written each word, turn over to check your spelling.

Adding e

4

Foxy is adding the letter **e** to his words. Can you help him? Read the words out loud. Then, add an **e** and listen to how the words change as you say them again. Practise spelling the new words on the dotted lines.

hat... › ....

bar... › ....

pin... › ....

Hey presto!

bit... › ....

Spot the vowels

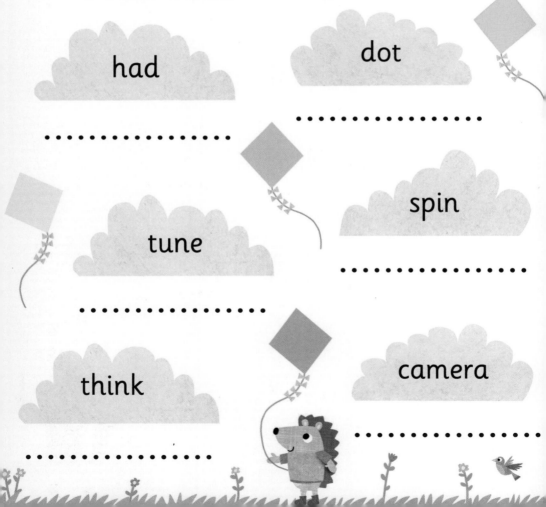

5

Vowels are the letters a, e, i, o and u. Draw a dot under the vowel or vowels in each word, to show Spike where they are. Then, cover the words and practise spelling them on the dotted lines.

had

dot

. . . .

. . . .

tune

spin

. . . .

. . . .

think

camera

. . . .

. . . .

ee wordsearch

Can you help Foxy and his friend find each of the words in the list at the bottom of the page? Words can be read downwards, across or diagonally. When you find a word, draw around it.

f	i	m	t	w	h	p
s	g	k	h	o	x	i
b	t	r	r	i	s	h
f	r	e	e	n	e	l
y	e	c	e	e	e	t
j	e	e	q	u	n	a
d	b	u	g	e	n	s

1. tree
2. free
3. three
4. been
5. seen
6. green

Missing endings

Help Squilly find the right letter to end each word
and write it in the space. Then, cover the words
and practise spelling them on the dotted lines.

g   m   p   b   r

w e ...

g u ...

d o ...

l i ...

f u ...

....

....

....

....

....

Words we often use

Say each word out loud and look at it carefully. Then, cover it and try spelling it on the dotted line. Uncover your word to check if your spelling is right. Turn the page over to practise again.

1 **he**

2 **she**

3 **me**

4 **we**

5 **be**

6 **they**

1 ....

2 ....

3 ....

4 ....

5 ....

6 ....

Twit twoo!

After you have written each word, turn over to check your spelling.

Words ending in ull

Moley needs to choose the right letters to finish her words, so her sentences make sense. Can you help her? Then, practise spelling the words on the dotted lines.

p   f   b

1. Moley is always ...ull of good ideas.

2. Bun's carrots are ready to ...ull out of the ground.

3. Moley's friend Biff is a ...ull, not a cow.

. . . .

Sounds like...

Some words sound the same but mean different things. Choose the right word to finish each sentence, then write it in the correct space.

bee

be

"If Coco leaves, I will .... alone," said Stripe.

The .... buzzed from flower to flower.

sew

so

"Will you teach me to ...., Spike?" asked Mo.

Hug was .... hungry, his tummy rumbled.

Quick quiz

Tick the correct spellings and put a cross by the
ones that are wrong. How many spellings have
Coco and Spike each got right?

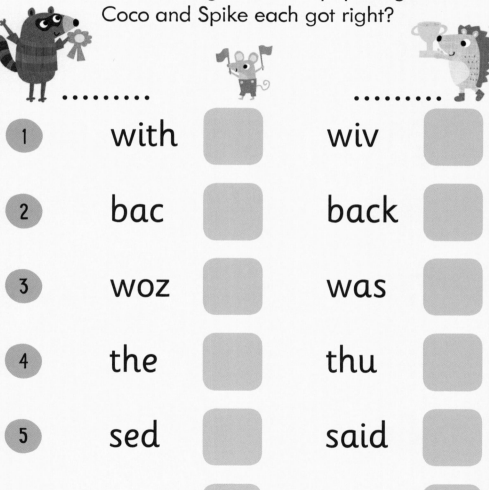

1 with   wiv

2 bac   back

3 woz   was

4 the   thu

5 sed   said

6 horse   hors

Missing beginnings

Help Mo choose the right letters from the boxes to start each
word. Then, practise the spellings on the dotted lines.

.....og

gl

.....ad

cr

.....ar

fr

.....ib

tr

.....ip

st

Bun's words

Can you help Bun finish these three-letter words using the vowels on her board? (Vowels are the letters a, e, i, o and u.) Choose **one** vowel that you can write on **all** the orange leaves to finish the four words.

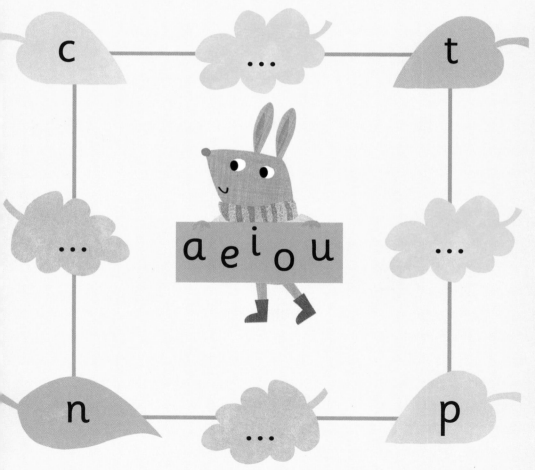

c ... t

... ...

a e i o u

n ... p

k, ke or ck?

You can use **k, ke** or **ck** to spell the **k** sound at the end of a word. Can you help Stripe choose **k** or **ck** to complete her words? Then, practise spelling the words under their correct letters.

b o o.....   c a.....e

k i.....   w o.....e

p e.....   c l o.....

k	ck
....	....
....	....
....	....

ff and zz words

Say each word out loud and look at it carefully.
Then, cover it and try spelling it on the dotted
line. Uncover your word to check if your spelling
is right. Turn the page over to practise again.

1 **puff**

....

2 **sniff**

....

3 **stuff**

....

4 **fizz**

....

5 **fuzz**

....

6 **buzz**

....

1

. . . .

2

. . . .

3

. . . .

4

. . . .

5

. . . .

6

. . . .

Twit twoo!

After you have written each word, turn over to check your spelling.

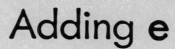

Foxy is adding the letter **e** to his words. Can you help him? Read the words out loud. Then, add an **e** and listen to how the words change as you say them again. Practise spelling the new words on the dotted lines.

hop... › ....

rob... › ....

hug... › ....

cut... › ....

Hey presto!

Spot the consonants

Consonants are any letters that are not vowels (a, e, i, o, u). Draw a dot under each consonant, to show Stripe where they are. Then, cover the words and practise spelling them on the dotted lines.

pan

got

· · · · · · · · · · · · · · · · · · ·

· · · · · · · · · · · · · · · · · · ·

pile

every

· · · · · · · · · · · · · · · · · · ·

· · · · · · · · · · · · · · · · · · ·

river

rainbow

· · · · · · · · · · · · · · · · ·

· · · · · · · · · · · · · · · · ·

oo wordsearch

Can you help Foxy and his friend find each of the words in the list at the bottom of the page? Words can be read downwards, across or diagonally. When you find a word, draw around it.

l	w	d	u	w	m	a
o	m	i	t	o	b	c
x	s	r	b	o	j	o
s	t	o	o	d	o	o
m	i	y	o	l	o	k
o	g	o	f	v	n	g
r	h	o	o	k	i	c

1 wood
2 hood
3 stood

4 cook
5 hook
6 took

Missing double letters

Help Spike find the right double letters to end each word and write them in the space. Then, cover the words and practise spelling them on the dotted lines.

ss   **ff**   **zz**   **gg**   **ll**

e ......

....

f l u ......

....

c a ......

....

g r a ......

....

f i ...... y

....

Words we often use

Say each word out loud and look at it carefully. Then, cover it and try spelling it on the dotted line. Uncover your word to check if your spelling is right. Turn the page over to practise again.

1 you

2 your

3 all

4 are

5 my

6 by

....

....

....

....

....

....

1 ....

2 ....

3 ....

4 ....

5 ....

6 ....

Twit twoo!

After you have written each word, turn over to check your spelling.

Words ending in nk

Moley needs to choose the right letters to finish her words, so her sentences make sense. Can you help her? Then, practise spelling the words on the dotted lines.

su   pi   ba

1. Walt the water rat lives in a hole in the .....nk of a river.

2. Moley's paws and nose are .....nk.

3. Oh no! Spike's new toy boat has .....nk.

. . . .

Sounds like...

Some words sound similar but mean different things. Choose the right word to finish each sentence, then write it in the correct space.

some

sum

Squilly found .... acorns on the ground.

"2 + 2 is an easy ....," said Olly.

one

won

"I will give Mo .... of my acorns," said Squilly.

Bun's team .... the hopping race.

Quick quiz

Tick the correct spellings and put a cross by the ones that are wrong. How many spellings have Coco and Spike each got right?

1   gone   gon

2   trubl   trouble

3   thing   fing

4   kitchen   kichun

5   count   cownt

6   thanks   thanx

Missing beginnings

Help Mo choose the right letters from the boxes to start each word. Then, practise the spellings on the dotted lines.

......it

....

pl

......ap

....

sp

......um

....

st

......ep

....

wh

......en

....

sn

Stripe's words

Can you help Stripe finish these three-letter words using the vowels on her board? (Vowels are the letters a, e, i, o and u.) Choose **one** vowel that you can write on **all** the orange leaves to finish the four words.

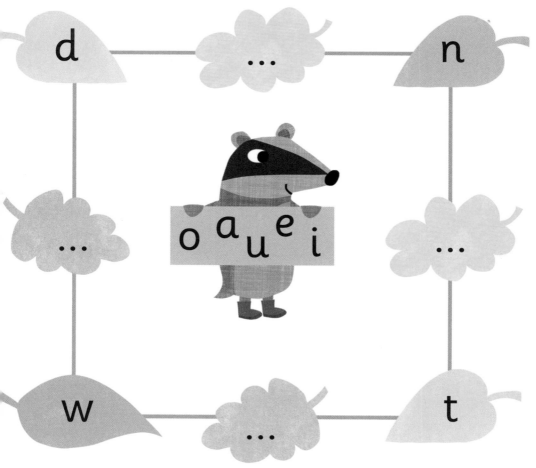

ai or ay?

26

Some sounds can be spelled in more than one way.
Can you help Coco choose **ai** or **ay** to complete
her words? Then, practise spelling the words
under their correct letters.

t r .....   b r ..... n

n l   a w .....

h .....   a f r ..... d

ai

ay

....

....

....

....

....

....

Words ending with **e** 27

Say each word out loud and look at it carefully.
Then, cover it and try spelling it on the dotted
line. Uncover your word to check if your spelling
is right. Turn the page over to practise again.

1 made   ....

2 make   ....

3 came   ....

4 time   ....

5 line   ....

6 like   ....

1

· ·

2

· ·

3

· ·

4

· ·

5

· ·

6

· ·

Twit twoo!

After you have written each word, turn over to check your spelling.

Adding s

Foxy is adding the letter **s** to his words to make them plural. (Plural means more than one of something.) Can you help him? Add an **s** to each word, then practise spelling the new words on the dotted lines.

spoon... › ....

cup... › ....

plate... › ....

bowl... › ....

Hey presto!

Two letters, one sound (29)

Some vowel sounds are made of two letters.
Draw a line under each vowel sound that is made
of two letters. Then, cover the words and practise
spelling them on the dotted lines.

goat

clue

. . . .

. . . .

sail

head

. . . .

. . . .

thief

dinosaur

. . . .

. . . .

ing wordsearch

Can you help Foxy and his friend find each of the words in the list at the bottom of the page? Words can be read downwards, across or diagonally. When you find a word, draw around it.

z	b	s	w	i	n	g
f	o	t	l	g	f	m
b	l	r	n	i	r	y
c	l	i	n	g	n	o
i	r	n	n	i	v	g
b	u	g	z	g	b	c
e	b	h	e	w	x	b

1 swing
2 sling
3 bring

4 fling
5 cling
6 string

Missing endings

Help Squilly find the right letters to end each word and write them in the space. Then, cover the words and practise spelling them on the dotted lines.

mp   lt   rd   nk   nt

d r i ....

l u ....

l e ....

w o ....

a d u ....

Words we often use

Say each word out loud and look at it carefully.
Then, cover it and try spelling it on the dotted
line. Uncover your word to check if your spelling
is right. Turn the page over to practise again.

1 is

2 his

3 has

4 was

5 says

6 said

....

....

....

....

....

....

1

....

2

....

3

....

4

....

5

....

6

....

Twit twoo!

After you have written each word, turn over to check your spelling.

Words ending with tch

Foxy needs to choose the right letters to finish his words, so his sentences make sense. Can you help him? Then, practise spelling the words on the dotted lines.

> ca   i   wa   scra

1 Hug used a stick to ....tch an ...tch on his foot.

2 Foxy ran home to find his ......tch.

3 Bun held up her paws to ......tch the ball.

Sounds like...

Some words sound the same but mean different things. Choose the right words to finish the sentences, then write them in the correct spaces.

 hare

 hair

"An animal's . . . . is called fur," said Olly.

Harriet the . . . . has longer ears than Bun.

 hear

 here

"If you come down . . . . it will be easier to

. . . . what I'm saying," shouted Spike to Olly.

Quick quiz

Tick the correct spellings and put a cross by the ones that are wrong. How many spellings have Coco and Spike each got right?

1 gud   good

2 children   childrun

3 field   feeld

4 pritee   pretty

5 uncle   uncl

6 glove   gluv

Missing middles

Help Mo choose the right letters from the boxes to finish each word. Then, practise the spellings on the dotted lines.

h.....p

....

c.....k

....

t.....m

....

g.....l

....

t.....nip

....

ur

ir

or

er

ar

Squilly's words

Can you help Squilly finish these three-letter words using the vowels on his board? (Vowels are the letters a, e, i, o and u.) Choose **one** vowel that you can write on **all** the orange leaves to finish the four words.

oi or oy?

Some sounds can be spelled in more than one way.
Can you help Coco choose **oi** or **oy** to complete
her words? Then, practise spelling the words
under their correct letters.

.....l   p.....n t

a n n.....   b.....

j.....   s.....l

oi   **oy**

. . . .

. . . .

. . . .

Words ending with e

Say each word out loud and look at it carefully. Then, cover it and try spelling it on the dotted line. Uncover your word to check if your spelling is right. Turn the page over to practise again.

1 home

2 hole

3 those

4 use

5 June

6 rule

1

....

2

....

3

....

4

....

5

....

6

....

Twit twoo!

After you have
written each word,
turn over to check
your spelling.

If a word ends in s, ss, x, zz, sh, or ch you make it plural by adding the letters **es**. (Plural means more than one of something.) Help Foxy add **es** to these words, then practise the spellings on the dotted lines.

bus.... › ....

wish.... › ....

lunch.... › ....

box.... › ....

Hey presto!

Spot the sound blends

Some consonants blend together to make a sound.
Underline each sound that is made of two consonants,
to show Foxy where they are. Then, cover the words
and practise spelling them on the dotted lines.

fish

chat

· · · · · · · · · · · · · · · · ·

· · · · · · · · · · · · · · · · ·

beach

thin

· · · · · · · · · · · · · · · · ·

· · · · · · · · · · · · · · · · ·

father

shocking

· · · · · · · · · · · · · · · · ·

· · · · · · · · · · · · · · · · ·

qu wordsearch

Can you help Foxy and his friend find each of the words in the list at the bottom of the page? Words can be read downwards, across or diagonally. When you find a word, draw around it.

q	u	e	e	n	i	q
u	u	n	q	q	k	q
a	a	i	u	t	z	u
c	e	u	c	i	u	i
k	q	c	u	k	u	l
n	u	q	u	i	e	t
q	u	r	l	e	q	u

1. quack
2. queen
3. quick
4. quiet
5. quilt
6. quiz

Making words

Some words are made by adding two words together. Help Hug make new words by drawing a line between words that make sense when you pair them together. Then, practise spelling the new words on the dotted lines.

bed	yard	....
note	noon	....
farm	room	....
after	corn	....
pop	paper	....

Words we often use

Say each word out loud and look at it carefully.
Then, cover it and try spelling it on the dotted
line. Uncover your word to check if your spelling
is right. Turn the page over to practise again.

1 so

2 no

3 go

4 little

5 help

6 from

1 ....

2 ....

3 ....

4 ....

5 ....

6 ....

Twit twoo!

After you have written each word, turn over to check your spelling.

Bun needs to choose the right letters to finish her words, so her sentences make sense. Can you help her? Then, practise spelling the words on the dotted lines.

ha   li   lo

1 Bun and her family .....ve in a sandy burrow.

2 Mo and Moley .....ve been friends for a long time.

3 Bun and Moley .....ve playing in the park.

Sounds like...

Some words sound the same but mean different things. Choose the right word to finish each sentence, then write it in the correct space.

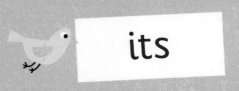

its

it's

Hug thinks .... a good day for a picnic.

The yellow bird flew back to .... nest.

see

sea

Olly's large eyes help him .... in the dark.

The river flowed down to the ....

Quick quiz

Tick the correct spellings and put a cross by the ones that are wrong. How many spellings have Coco and Spike each got right?

1. alone   aloan

2. gurl   girl

3. once   wons

4. wil   will

5. poot   put

6. skool   school

Missing letters

Help Mo choose the right letters from the boxes to finish eac
word. Then, practise the spellings on the dotted lines.

t...b...

....

i e

t...k...

....

e e

f...v...

....

u e

j...k...

....

a e

th...m...

....

o e

Bun's words

Can you help Bun finish these three-letter words using the vowels on her board? (Vowels are the letters a, e, i, o and u.) Choose **one** vowel that you can write on **all** the orange leaves to finish the four words.

s ... n

... i o e a u ...

b ... w

ee or ea?

Some sounds can be spelled in more than one way.
Can you help Squilly choose **ee** or **ea** to complete
his words? Then, practise spelling the words
under their correct letters.

f.....l   s.....k   .....sy

gr.....dy

m.....n   dr.....m

ee

ea

. . . .

. . . .

. . . .

sh and ch words

Say each word out loud and look at it carefully.
Then, cover it and try spelling it on the dotted
line. Uncover your word to check if your spelling
is right. Turn the page over to practise again.

1   shin

2   ship

3   shop

4   chin

5   chip

6   chop

1

. . . .

2

. . . .

3

. . . .

4

. . . .

5

. . . .

6

. . . .

Twit twoo!

After you have
written each word,
turn over to check
your spelling.

Adding y

Foxy is adding **y** to these words to change their
meaning. Can you help him? Read the words out loud.
Change the words by adding **y**, then say them again.
Practise spelling the new words on the dotted lines.

sand... › ....

wind... › ....

snow... › ....

rain... › ....

Hey
presto!

Can you help Spike spot the sounds in these words?
Draw a **dot** under the sounds that are made by a
single letter. Next, draw a **line** under the sounds
made from **two letters.** Then, cover the words and
practise spelling them on the dotted lines.

duck

boot

. . . .

. . . .

cash

horn

. . . .

. . . .

cheat

teeth

. . . .

. . . .

Plurals wordsearch

54

Add an **s** to each word at the bottom of the page to make
t plural, then help Foxy and his friend find the new words.
Words can be read downwards, across or diagonally.
When you find a word, draw around it.

n	e	e	d	l	e	s
o	o	c	n	e	k	h
t	r	e	o	n	d	o
d	o	s	u	n	s	o
l	o	r	s	s	e	t
n	t	w	i	g	s	s
d	s	g	k	k	c	n

1 twig...

2 trunk...

3 shoot...

4 cone...

5 root...

6 needle...

Find the rhyme

Words that rhyme, such as **red** and **bed**, have the same
ending sound. Can you help Spike find pairs of rhyming
words? Draw a line between the words that rhyme.
Then, practise the spellings on the dotted lines.

dear

song

bake

fear

long

frown

town

sight

fright

lake

Words we often use

Say each word out loud and look at it carefully.
Then, cover it and try spelling it on the dotted
line. Uncover your word to check if your spelling
is right. Turn the page over to practise again.

1 this

2 them

3 then

4 that

5 these

6 please

1 ....

2 ....

3 ....

4 ....

5 ....

6 ....

After you have
written each word,
turn over to check
your spelling.

Twit twoo!

Moley needs to choose the right letters to finish her words, so her sentences make sense. Can you help her? Then, practise spelling the words on the dotted lines.

---

ri   wi   si

---

1 Olly the owl has hurt the tip of his ....ng.

2 The animals danced in a ....ng around the tree.

3 Moley loves to paint and Hug loves to ....ng.

Sounds like...

Some words sound the same but mean different things. Choose the right word to finish each sentence, then write it in the correct space.

too

two

"Can I come . . . .?" asked Hug.

Bun ate . . . . carrots for lunch.

saw

sore

The cut on Stripe's leg looked . . . .

Foxy . . . . his friend sitting on a log.

Quick quiz

Tick the correct spellings and put a cross by the ones that are wrong. How many spellings have Coco and Spike each got right?

....

1. hows   [ ]   house   [ ]
2. tooday   [ ]   today   [ ]
3. pairunt   [ ]   parent   [ ]
4. skin   [ ]   scin   [ ]
5. fonics   [ ]   phonics [ ]
6. menny   [ ]   many   [ ]

Missing endings

Help Mo choose the right letters from the boxes to finish each word. Then, practise the spellings on the dotted lines.

b e f........

....

g l........

....

s e c........

....

t h........

....

a d m........

....

are

ere

ire

ore

ure

Stripe's words

Can you help Stripe finish these three-letter words using the vowels on her board? (Vowels are the letters a, e, i, o and u.) Choose **one** vowel that you can write on **all** the orange leaves to finish the four words.

oa or oe?

Some sounds can be spelled in more than one way.
Can you help Coco choose **oa** or **oe** to complete
her words? Then, practise spelling the words
under their correct letters.

b.....t   m.....n

t.....   w.....

g.....s   t.....d

oa   oe

....

....

....

Words with **ai** and **ay**

Say each word out loud and look at it carefully. Then, cover it and try spelling it on the dotted line. Uncover your word to check if your spelling is right. Turn the page over to practise again.

1 **pain** ....

2 **stain** ....

3 **sprain** ....

4 **pay** ....

5 **stay** ....

6 **spray** ....

1

· ·

2

· ·

3

· ·

4

· ·

5

· ·

6

· ·

Twit twoo!

After you have written each word, turn over to check your spelling.

Adding ing

Foxy is adding **ing** to these words to change their meaning. Can you help him? Read the words out loud. Change the words by adding **ing,** then say them again. Practise spelling the new words on the dotted lines.

eat...... > ....

sleep..... > ....

work.... > ....

play..... > ....

Hey presto!

Counting syllables

Stripe is saying words out loud to see how many syllables (or beats) they have. Count the syllables in the words and draw a line to the kite with the right number. Then, cover and practise spelling the words.

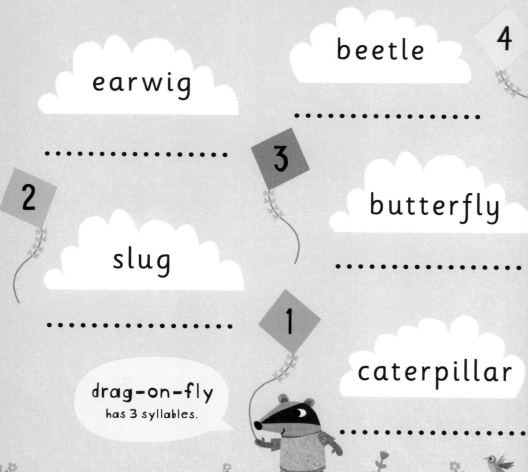

beetle

earwig

4

3

2

butterfly

slug

1

caterpillar

drag-on-fly
has 3 syllables.

Plurals wordsearch

Add **es** to each word at the bottom of the page to make it plural. Can you help Foxy and his friend find the new words? Words can be read downwards, across or diagonally. When you find a word, draw around it.

v	b	t	a	x	e	s
l	z	u	q	b	e	s
g	l	a	s	s	e	s
v	f	l	s	h	e	v
u	d	o	s	x	e	p
c	r	i	o	h	b	s
c	d	f	a	c	h	l

1 tax.....

2 fox.....

3 bush.....

4 dish.....

5 glass.....

6 cross.....

Write a rhyme

Words that rhyme, such as **red** and b**ed**, have the same
ending sound. Can you help Squilly make pairs of rhymin
words? Write a three-letter word that rhymes with each
word on his signs. Check the answers at the back of the
pad, then practise the spellings at the bottom of the page.

m a t

....

f u n

....

t u b

....

f o g

....

c a r

....

....

....

Words we often use

68

Say each word out loud and look at it carefully.
Then, cover it and try spelling it on the dotted
line. Uncover your word to check if your spelling
is right. Turn the page over to practise again.

1. **one**

2. **have**

3. **come**

4. **some**

5. **were**

6. **there**

1 ....

2 ....

3 ....

4 ....

5 ....

6 ....

Twit twoo!

After you have written each word, turn over to check your spelling.

sw words

Spike needs to choose the right letters to finish his words, so his sentences make sense. Can you help him? Then, practise spelling the words on the dotted lines.

im   ay   an

1 Spike watched the fish sw...... in the river.

2 Then, he saw a sw...... with a long, white neck.

3 The willow trees began to sw...... in the breeze.

· · · · · · · · · · · · ·   · · · · · · · · · · · ·   · · · · · · · · · · ·

Some words sound similar but mean different things. Choose the right word to finish each sentence, then write it in the correct space.

for

four

Foxy has ········· legs and a bushy tail.

"What is that basket ········· ?" asked Mo.

of

off

Spike and Coco are the best ········· friends.

The wind blew Moley's hat ··········

Quick quiz

Tick the correct spellings and put a cross by the ones that are wrong. How many spellings have Coco and Spike each got right?

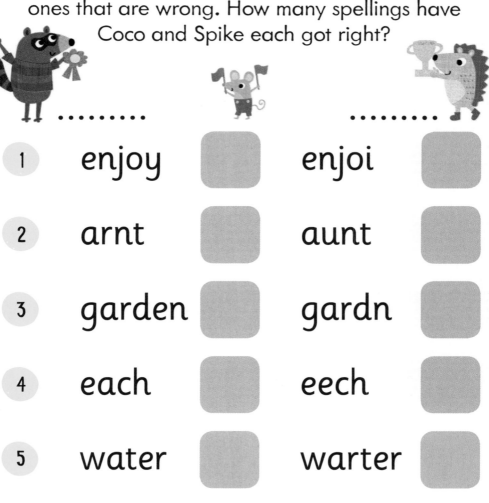

1	enjoy		enjoi	
2	arnt		aunt	
3	garden		gardn	
4	each		eech	
5	water		warter	
6	agen		again	

Missing middles

Help Mo choose the right letters from the boxes to finish each word. Then, practise the spellings on the dotted lines.

t.......t

air

....

ch.......ful

ear

....

cl.......s

eer

....

keyb.......d

igh

....

f.......ly

oar

....

Squilly's words

Can you help Squilly finish these three-letter words using the vowels on his board? (Vowels are the letters a, e, i, o and u.) Write a **different** vowel on each orange leaf to finish the four words. Circle the vowel that is not used.

t ... b

... e a u i o ...

y ... s

er or ir?

Some sounds can be spelled in more than one way.
Can you help Stripe choose **er** or **ir** to complete
her words? Then, practise spelling the words
under their correct middle letters.

h.....s   p.....son

f.....st   sk.....t

g.....m   th.....d

er

ir

oi words

Say each word out loud and look at it carefully. Then, cover it and try spelling it on the dotted line. Uncover your word to check if your spelling is right. Turn the page over to practise again.

1 boil ....

2 coil ....

3 join ....

4 voice ....

5 noise ....

6 toilet ....

1

. . . .

2

. . . .

3

. . . .

4

. . . .

5

. . . .

6

. . . .

After you have written each word, turn over to check your spelling.

Twit twoo!

Foxy is adding **ed** to his words to change their meaning. Can you help him? Read the words out loud. Change the words by adding **ed**, then say them again. Practise spelling the new words on the dotted lines.

look..... › ....

fill..... › ....

ask.... › ....

hiss.... › ....

Hey presto!

Spot the mistake

Each of the words below has an extra letter in it.
See if you can help Spike find the mistakes. Draw
around the extra letter, check the answer, then
practise the correct spellings on the dotted lines.

sillver

fatt

. . . .

. . . .

stopp

bagg

. . . .

. . . .

mudd

panncake

. . . .

. . . .

Adding y wordsearch

Add a y to each word at the bottom of the page to change its meaning. Then, help Foxy and his friend find the new words. Words can be read downwards, across or diagonally. When you find a word, draw around it.

c	y	e	l	w	s	p
r	h	b	u	m	p	y
y	y	i	r	p	e	l
z	s	m	l	r	e	e
t	e	c	o	l	d	a
u	d	i	r	t	y	f
b	v	l	u	c	k	y

1. leaf...
2. bump...
3. chill....
4. luck...
5. speed...
6. dirt...

Count the syllables

Can you help Spike count the syllables (or beats) in the words on the signs? Say each word out loud to hear how many syllables it has. Count the syllables in each word and draw a line to the birdhouse with the right number. Then, practise spelling the words.

1

2

3

4

crocodile

alligator

mouse

squirrel

. . . .

. . . .

. . . .

. . . .

Words we often use

Say each word out loud and look at it carefully. Then, cover it and try spelling it on the dotted line. Uncover your word to check if your spelling is right. Turn the page over to practise again.

1 do

2 to

3 on

4 their

5 people

6 very

1 ....

2 ....

3 ....

4 ....

5 ....

6 ....

Twit twoo!

After you have written each word, turn over to check your spelling.

tw words

Coco needs to choose the right letters to finish her words, so her sentences make sense. Can you help her? Then, practise spelling the words on the dotted lines.

ist	in	ice

1 Squilly watched the leaves tw....... and twirl in the wind.

2 Coco ran tw....... as fast as Stripe in the race.

3 Bun's tw...... sister looks just like her.

· · · · · · · · · · 　　　 · · · · · · · · · · 　　　 · · · · · · · · · ·

Sounds like...

Some words sound the same but mean different things. Choose the right word to finish each sentence, then write it in the correct space.

 rode   road

Spike looks both ways when he crosses a . . . .

"I . . . . a horse once," squeaked Mo.

 blew   blue

Moley's hat and glasses are . . . .

Stripe . . . . out all her birthday candles.

Quick quiz

83

Tick the correct spellings and put a cross by the ones that are wrong. How many spellings have Coco and Spike each got right?

. . . .

1 apon   upon

2 difrent   different

3 a   u

4 yor   your

5 love   luv

6 hav   have

Long o sounds

Help Mo choose the right letters from the boxes to finish each word. Then, practise the spellings on the dotted lines.

st...n...

....

o

g.....s

....

o w

g.....l

....

o   e

gr.....

....

o a

r...bot

....

o e

Stripe's words

Can you help Stripe finish these three-letter words using the consonants on her board? (A consonant is any letter that is not a, e, i, o or u.) Write each consonant from her board on a green leaf to finish the four words.

igh or ie?

Some sounds can be spelled in more than one way.
Can you help Coco choose **igh** or **ie** to complete
her words? Then, practise spelling the words
under their correct letters.

cr......d   br......t

l......s   n......t

p......   r......t

igh

ie

. . . .

. . . .

. . . .

ow words

Say each word out loud and look at it carefully. Then, cover it and try spelling it on the dotted line. Uncover your word to check if your spelling is right. Turn the page over to practise again.

1 **howl**

2 **growl**

3 **prowl**

4 **gown**

5 **brown**

6 **crown**

1

....

2

....

3

....

4

....

5

....

6

....

Twit twoo!

After you have
written each word,
turn over to check
your spelling.

Adding er

Foxy is adding **er** to his words to change their meaning. Can you help him? Read the words out loud. Change the words by adding **er,** then say them again. Practise spelling the new words on the dotted lines.

slow.... › ....

fast.... › ....

poor... › ....

rich.... › ....

Hey presto!

Spot the mistake

Each word below has one letter missing. See if you can help Foxy find the mistakes. Draw around the letter that should be a double letter, check the answers, then practise the correct spellings on the dotted lines.

eg

clas

. . . .

. . . .

rabit

pilow

. . . .

. . . .

sory

funy

. . . .

. . . .

Adding ed wordsearch (90)

Add **ed** to each word at the bottom of the page to change its meaning. Can you help Foxy and his friend find the new words? Words can be read downwards, across or diagonally. When you find a word, draw around it.

l	i	i	w	d	j	s
f	i	f	a	r	d	p
f	z	c	l	e	v	u
p	i	c	k	e	d	m
g	w	l	e	e	p	p
z	a	x	d	j	d	e
t	j	u	m	p	e	d

1 jump.....

2 pump.....

3 walk.....

4 talk.....

5 pick.....

6 lick.....

Find a rhyme

Words that rhyme, such as h**ead** and fl**ed**, have the same ending sound, but the sound may have different spellings. Can you help Squilly find pairs of rhyming words? Draw a line between the words that rhyme. Then, practise the spellings on the dotted lines.

tail

die

main

flow

gate

try

wait

pale

lane

oh

....

....

wh words we often use

Say each word out loud and look at it carefully. Then, cover it and try spelling it on the dotted line. Uncover your word to check if your spelling is right. Turn the page over to practise again.

1. when

2. where

3. what

4. why

5. who

6. whose

1 . . . .

2 . . . .

3 . . . .

4 . . . .

5 . . . .

6 . . . .

Twit twoo!

After you have
written each word,
turn over to check
your spelling.

wr words

Moley needs to choose the right letters to finish her words, so her sentences make sense. Can you help her? Then, practise spelling the words on the dotted lines.

ite   ote   ong

1 Spellings are easier to learn when you wr....... them down.

2 Some spellings look wr....... even when they are right.

3 Moley wr....... a long letter to her uncle.

Sounds like...

Some words sound similar but mean different things. Choose the right word to finish each sentence, then write it in the correct space.

by

buy

Spike saved up his money to .... some marbles

Bun's book is .... a famous writer.

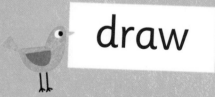

draw

drawer

Can you .... another bird on this page?

Moley keeps her clean clothes in a ....

Quick quiz

95

Tick the correct spellings and put a cross by the ones that are wrong. How many spellings have Coco and Spike each got right?

. . . .

1 poosh   push

2 eny   any

3 thank   fank

4 hoam   home

5 spell   spel

6 hur   her

Long e sounds

Help Mo choose the right letters from the boxes to finish each word. Then, practise the spellings on the dotted lines.

s....t

....

str....t

....

ch....f

....

boss...

....

p....ple

....

ee

y

ea

eo

ie

Bun's words

Can you help Bun finish these three-letter words using the consonants on her board? (A consonant is any letter that is not a, e, i, o or u.) Write each consonant on a green leaf to finish the four words. (There's more than one answer.)

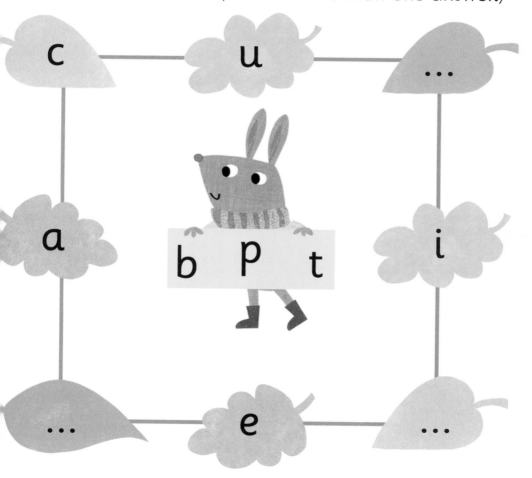

ue or ew?

Some sounds can be spelled in more than one way.
Can you help Squilly choose **ue** or **ew** to complete
his words? Then, practise spelling the words
under their correct letters.

gl.....   ch.....

f.....   tr.....

T.....sday   dr.....

ue   **ew**

. . . .

. . . .

. . . .

ou words

Say each word out loud and look at it carefully. Then, cover it and try spelling it on the dotted line. Uncover your word to check if your spelling is right. Turn the page over to practise again.

1 loud

2 cloud

3 shout

4 out

5 found

6 around

1

....

2

....

3

....

4

....

5

....

6

....

Twit twoo!

After you have
written each word,
turn over to check
your spelling.

Adding est

Foxy is adding **est** to his words to change their meaning. Can you help him? Read the words out loud. Change the words by adding **est,** then say them again. Practise spelling the new words on the dotted lines.

short...... > ....

tall...... > ....

new...... > ....

old...... > ....

Hey presto!

Spot the mistake

Two letters in each word are the wrong way around. Can you help Spike find the mistakes? Draw around the letters that have been reversed, check the answers, then practise the correct spellings on the dotted lines.

chiar

freind

littel

screne

raod

thikc

Adding er wordsearch

Add **er** to each word at the bottom of the page to change its meaning. Can you help Foxy and his friend find the new words? Words can be read downwards, across or diagonally. When you find a word, draw around it.

```
g  d  f  i  h  c  l
d  r  a  l  m  h  o
h  k  e  r  w  i  w
z  v  m  a  k  o  e
l  i  g  h  t  e  r
s  m  a  l  l  e  r
k  h  i  g  h  e  r
```

1 small.....   4 dark.....

2 great.....   5 low.....

3 light.....   6 high.....

Write a rhyme

Words that rhyme, such as **sung** and **rung**, have the
same ending sound. Help Squilly write a four-letter word
that rhymes with each word on his signs. Check the
answers at the back of the pad, then practise
the spellings at the bottom of the page.

park

bend

link

ring

tent

Words we often use

Say each word out loud and look at it carefully.
Then, cover it and try spelling it on the dotted
line. Uncover your word to check if your spelling
is right. Turn the page over to practise again.

1. if
2. us
3. bus
4. yes
5. gas
6. pal

1 ....

2 ....

3 ....

4 ....

5 ....

6 ....

Twit twoo!

After you have
written each word,
turn over to check
your spelling.

Moley needs to choose the right letters to finish her words, so her sentences make sense. Can you help her? Then, practise spelling the words on the dotted lines.

> ale   eel   ite

1 The blue wh........ is the largest animal on Earth.

2 Snow had turned the fields all wh........

3 A wh........ fell off Moley's toy bus.

Sounds like...

Some words sound similar but mean different things. Choose the right word to finish each sentence, then write it in the correct space.

our

hour

Stripe's cake needs to cook for one ....

"Look at .... kites!" shouted Foxy and Spike.

flour

flower

Stripe made a cake from sugar, butter and ....

Coco gave Squilly a .... from her garden.

Tick the correct spellings and put a cross by the ones that are wrong. How many spellings have Coco and Spike each got right?

·········   ·········

1 frend [ ]   friend [ ]

2 please [ ]   plees [ ]

3 becos [ ]   because [ ]

4 when [ ]   wen [ ]

5 whair [ ]   where [ ]

6 people [ ]   peeple [ ]

or sounds

Help Mo choose the right letters from the boxes to finish ea
word. Then, practise the spellings on the dotted lines.

b.....n

....

r......

....

d.......

....

s.....ce

....

sn.......

....

au

or

ore

aw

oor

Stripe's words

Can you help Stripe finish these three-letter words using the consonants on her board? (A consonant is any letter that is not a, e, i, o or u.) Write each consonant on a green leaf to finish the four words.

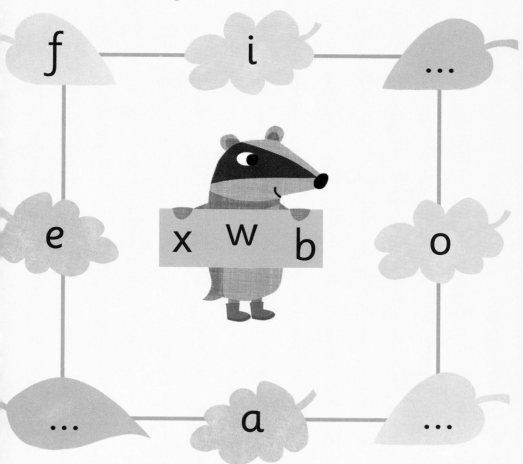

ow or ou?

Some sounds can be spelled in more than one way.
Can you help Coco choose **ow** or **ou** to complete
her words? Then, practise spelling the words
under their correct letters.

.....l   m.....th

.....ch   c.....

s.....nd   d.....n

ow   **ou**

....

....

....

Words ending with er

Say each word out loud and look at it carefully. Then, cover it and try spelling it on the dotted line. Uncover your word to check if your spelling is right. Turn the page over to practise again.

1. better ....

2. under ....

3. summer ....

4. winter ....

5. sister ....

6. brother ....

1 ....

2 ....

3 ....

4 ....

5 ....

6 ....

Twit twoo!

After you have written each word, turn over to check your spelling.

Adding un

Foxy is adding **un** to his words to change their meaning. Can you help him? Read the words out loud. Change the words by adding **un**, then say them again. Practise spelling the new words on the dotted lines.

....even › ....

....well › ....

...fair › ....

....kind › ....

Hey presto!

Spot the mistake

One letter in each clothes word below is wrong. See if you can help Stripe find the mistakes. Draw around the letters that are wrong, check the answers, then practise the correct spellings on the dotted lines.

shurt

coet

· · · · · · · · · · · · · · · · · ·

· · · · · · · · · · · · · · · · · ·

skarf

shoos

· · · · · · · · · · · · · · · · · ·

· · · · · · · · · · · · · · · · · ·

sokks

jeanz

· · · · · · · · · · · · · · · · · ·

· · · · · · · · · · · · · · · · · ·

Adding **un** wordsearch  114

Add **un** to each word at the bottom of the page to change its meaning. Can you help Foxy and his friend find the new words? Words can be read downwards, across or diagonally. When you find a word, draw around it.

u	n	d	r	e	s	s
n	p	d	a	d	e	u
p	u	l	u	e	n	n
a	u	e	i	p	s	f
c	k	t	u	n	d	o
k	n	i	n	u	g	l
u	n	l	o	c	k	d

1 ......do   4 .....tie

2 ......pack   5 .....lock

3 ......dress   6 ....fold

Count the syllables

Can you help Spike count the syllables (or beats) in the words on the signs? Say each word out loud to hear how many syllables it has. Count the syllables in each word and draw a line to the birdhouse with the right number. Then, practise spelling the words.

1   2   3   4

coconut

apple

banana

pear

Words we often use

Say each word out loud and look at it carefully. Then, cover it and try spelling it on the dotted line. Uncover your word to check if your spelling is right. Turn the page over to practise again.

1 **don't**

....

2 **won't**

....

3 **can't**

....

4 **Mr**

....

5 **Mrs**

....

6 **should**

....

1 ....

2 ....

3 ....

4 ....

5 ....

6 ....

Twit twoo!

After you have written each word, turn over to check your spelling.

Moley needs to choose the right letters to finish these words, so her sentences make sense. Can you help her? Then, practise spelling the words on the dotted lines.

> oto   onics   one

1. The animals are learning ph.............

2. Hug has a ph........ of all his friends on his shelf.

3. Mo's ph........ rang six times, then stopped.

Sounds like...

Some words sound similar but mean different things. Choose the right word to finish each sentence, then write it in the correct space.

 wear **where**

"Which scarf shall I .... today?" asked Mo.

Spike has forgotten .... he put his marbles.

 there **their**

Hug and Bun put .... apples in a basket.

"Are .... enough apples for us all?" asked Mo

Quick quiz

Tick the correct spellings and put a cross by the ones that are wrong. How many spellings have Coco and Spike each got right?

....

1. group ☐   groop ☐
2. doant ☐   don't ☐
3. very ☐   verry ☐
4. bruvver ☐   brother ☐
5. about ☐   abowt ☐
6. can't ☐   carnt ☐

Word list

This list contains all the words in the pad. You can use it to find out how words are spelled and to test yourself to see which spellings you can remember.

a

a
about
admire
adult
afraid
after
afternoon
again
all
alligator
alone
annoy
any
apple
are
around
ask
asked
aunt
away

b

back
bag
bake
banana
bank
bar
bare
bark
bat
be
beach
because
bed
bedroom
bee
been
beetle
before
bend
bent
bet
better

big
bit
bite
blew
blue
boat
bog
boil
book
boot
born
bossy
bow
bowl
bowls
box
boxes
boy
brain
bright
bring
brother
brown

bull
bump
bumpy
bun
bus
buses
bush
bushes
butterfly
buy
buzz
by

c

cab
cake
call
came
camera
can
can't
cap
car

Word list

cash
cat
catch
caterpillar
chair
chat
cheat
cheerful
chew
chief
children
chill
chilly
chin
chip
chop
class
clears
cling
clock
cloud
clue
coat
coconut
cog
coil
come
cone

cones
cook
cork
corn
count
cow
crib
cried
crocodile
cross
crosses
crown
cub
cup
cups
curl
cut
cute

d

dark
darker
dear
den
dent
dew
die
different

dinosaur
dirt
dirty
dish
dishes
do
dog
don't
door
dot
down
dragonfly
draw
drawer
dream
dress
drew
drink
duck

e

each
earwig
easy
eat
eating
egg
enjoy

even
every

f

fair
fairly
far
farm
farmyard
fast
faster
fat
father
fear
feel
fend
few
fib
field
fill
filled
fin
first
fish
five
fizz
fizzy
fling

Word list

flour
flow
flower
fluff
fog
fold
for
found
four
fox
foxes
free
friend
fright
frog
from
frown
full
fun
funny
fur
fuzz

g
garden
gas
gate
germ

girl
glad
glare
glass
glasses
glove
glue
go
goal
goat
goes
gone
good
got
gown
grass
great
greater
greedy
green
group
grow
growl
gum
gun

h
had
hair
hare
hark
harp
has
hat
hate
have
hay
he
head
hear
help
her
here
hers
high
higher
hill
him
his
hiss
hissed
hog
hole
home

hood
hook
hop
hope
horn
horse
hour
house
howl
hub
hug
huge
hum
hut

i
if
ill
is
itch
it's
its

j
jar
jeans
jog
join

Word list

joke
joy
jump
jumped
June

k
keep
key
keyboard
kick
kind
king
kink
kitchen
kite

l
lake
lane
lark
leaf
leafy
leg
lend
lent
lick
licked

lies
light
lighter
like
line
link
lip
little
live
lock
log
long
look
looked
loud
love
low
lower
luck
lucky
lump
lunch
lunches

m
made
main
make

many
mark
mat
me
mean
mend
mess
met
mink
miss
moan
mop
moss
mouse
mouth
Mr
Mrs
mud
mug
my

n
nail
nap
needle
needles
net
new

newest
night
no
noise
noon
note
notepaper
now
nun
nut

o
of
off
oh
oil
old
oldest
on
once
one
ouch
our
out
owl

p
pack

Word list

		r	s
pain	pit	rabbit	said
pal	plate	rain	sail
pale	plates	rainbow	sand
pan	play	rainy	sandy
pancake	playing	rat	sat
paper	please	raw	sauce
parent	plum	rent	saw
park	point	rib	says
pat	poor	rich	scarf
pay	poorer	richer	school
pear	pop	right	scratch
peck	popcorn	ring	screen
people	pretty	rink	sea
person	prowl	rip	seat
pet	puff	river	secure
phone	pull	road	see
phonics	pump	rob	seek
photo	pumped	robe	seen
pick	push	robot	send
picked	put	rode	sent
pie		room	sew
pig	**q**	root	she
pile	quack	roots	shin
pill	queen	rub	ship
pillow	quick	rule	shirt
pin	quiet	run	shocking
pine	quilt	rut	shoes
pink	quiz		

Word list

shoot	sob	stuff	that
shoots	socks	sum	the
shop	soil	summer	their
short	some	sun	them
shortest	son	sunk	theme
should	song	swan	then
shout	sore	sway	there
sight	sorry	swim	these
silver	sound	swing	they
sing	speed		thick
sink	speedy	†	thief
sister	spell	tab	thin
skin	spin	tail	thing
skirt	spit	take	think
sleep	spoon	talk	third
sleeping	spoons	talked	this
sling	sprain	tall	those
slow	spray	tallest	three
slower	squirrel	tap	tie
slug	stain	tar	tight
small	star	tax	time
smaller	stay	taxes	to
snap	step	teeth	toad
sniff	stone	tend	today
snore	stood	tent	toe
snow	stop	term	toilet
snowy	street	thank	too
so	string	thanks	took

Word list

town
toy
tray
tree
trip
trouble
true
trunk
trunks
try
tub
tube
Tuesday
tug
tune
turnip
twice
twig
twigs
twin
twist
two

U

uncle
under
undo
undress

uneven
unfair
unfold
unkind
unlock
unpack
untie
unwell
upon
us
use

V

vat
vent
very
voice

W

wait
walk
walked
was
watch
water
wax
we
wear

web
well
went
were
wet
whale
what
wheel
when
where
white
who
whose
why
will
wind
windy
wing
wink

winter
wish
wishes
with
woe
woke
won
won't
wood
word
work
working
write
wrong
wrote

Y

yard
yes
you
your

> Cover the words and test yourself to see which spellings you can remember.

Answers

leg, fin, mop, nut, yes
car, cog, curl; key, keep, king
hate, bare, pine, bite
had, dot, tune, spin, think, camera

web, gum, dog, lip, fur
full, pull, bull
be, bee; sew, so
Correct = with, back, was, the, said, horse (Coco 3, Spike 3)
frog, glad, star, crib, trip
cat, tap, can, nap
book, cake, woke; kick, peck, clock
hope, robe, huge, cute
pan, pile, river, got, every, rainbow

19 egg, fluff, call, grass, fizzy
21 bank, pink, sunk
22 some, sum; one, won
23 Correct = gone, trouble, thing, kitchen, count, thanks (Coco 5, Spike 1)
24 spit, snap, plum, step, when
25 den, net, dew, wet
26 nail, brain, afraid; tray, away, hay
28 spoons, cups, plates, bowls
29 goat, clue, sail, head, thief, dinosaur
30
31 drink, lump, lent, word, adult
33 scratch, itch, watch, catch
34 hair, hare; here, hear
35 Correct = good, children, field, pretty, uncle, glove (Coco 4, Spike 2)
36 harp, cork, term, girl, turnip
37 rip, pig, rib, big
38 oil, point, soil; annoy, joy, boy

Answers

40 buses, wishes, lunches, boxes
41 fish, chat, beach, thin, father, shocking
42

43 bedroom, notepaper, farmyard,
    afternoon, popcorn
45 live, have, love
46 it's, its; see, sea
47 Correct = alone, girl, once, will,
    put, school (Coco 2, Spike 4)
48 tube, take, five, joke, theme
49 son, now, sob, bow
50 feel, seek, greedy; easy, mean, dream
52 sandy, windy, snowy, rainy
53 duck, horn, cheat, boot, cash, teeth
54 twigs, trunks, shoots
    cones, roots, needles

55 dear–fear, bake–lake,
    long–song, town–frown,
    fright–sight
57 wing, ring, sing
58 too, two; sore, saw
59 Correct = house, today, parent,
    skin, phonics, many
    (Coco 1, Spike 5)
60 before, glare, secure,
    there, admire
61 hum, mug, hut, tug
62 boat, toad, moan; toe, goes, w
64 eating, sleeping, working,
    playing
65 ear/wig (2),
    slug (1),
    bee/tle (2),
    but/ter/fly (3),
    cat/er/pill/ar (4)
66 taxes   dishes
    foxes   glasses
    bushes   crosses

Answers

57 Answers include:
bat, cat, fat, hat, pat, rat, sat, tat, vat
bun, gun, nun, pun, run, sun
cub, dub, hub, nub, pub, rub, sub
bog, cog, dog, hog, jog, log
bar, far, jar, par, tar

79 swim, swan, sway

80 four, for; of, off

81 Correct = enjoy, aunt, garden, each, water, again (Coco 4, Spike 2)

82 tight, cheerful, clears, keyboard, fairly

83 tab, bus, toy, yes (Circle i)

84 hers, person, germ; first, skirt, third

86 looked, filled, asked, hissed

87 l silver, t fat, p stop,
g bag, d mud, n pancake

88 leafy   lucky
bumpy   speedy
chilly   dirty

89 cro/co/dile (3), al/li/ga/tor (4),
mouse (1), squi/rrel (2),

91 twist, twice, twin

82 road, rode; blue, blew

83 Correct = upon, different, a,
your, love, have (Coco 2,
Spike 4)

84 stone, goes, goal, grow, robot

85 him, met, her, rut

86 bright, night, right;
cried, lies, pie

88 slower, faster, poorer, richer

89 g egg, s class, b rabbit,
l pillow, r sorry, n funny

90 jumped   talked
pumped   picked
walked   licked

91 tail–pale, die–try, main–lane,
flow–oh, gate–wait

93 write, wrong, wrote

94 buy, by; draw, drawer

95 Correct = push, any, thank,
home, spell, her
(Coco 2, Spike 4)

96 seat, street, chief, bossy, people

Answers

97 cub/cup, bit/pit,
    cap/cab, pet/bet

98 glue, true, Tuesday;
    chew, few, drew

100 shortest, tallest, newest, oldest

101 chiar > chair,   freind > friend,
    littel > little,   screne > screen,
    raod > road,   thikc > thick

102 smaller, greater, lighter
    darker, lower, higher

103 Answers include:
    bark, dark, hark, lark, mark
    fend, lend, mend, pend, rend, send,
    tend, vend, wend
    kink, mink, pink, rink, sink, wink
    ding, king, ling, ping, sing, wing
    bent, dent, gent, lent, pent, rent,
    sent, vent, went

105 whale, white, wheel

106 hour, our; flour, flower

107 Correct = friend, please, because,
    when, where, people (Coco 3, Spike 3)

108 born, raw, door, sauce, snore

109 fib, box, few, wax

110 owl, cow, down;
    ouch, sound, mouth

112 uneven, unwell, unfair,
    unkind

113 shurt > shirt,   coet > coat,
    skarf > scarf,   shoos > shoes
    sokks > socks, jeanz > jeans

114 undo, unpack, undress
    untie, unlock, unfold

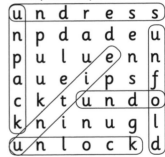

115 co/co/nut (3), ba/na/na (3)
    app/le (2), pear (1)

117 phonics, photo, phone

118 wear, where; their, there

119 Correct = group, don't, very,
    brother, about, can't
    (Coco 4, Spike 2)